The Story Of Christmas

Christmas Countdown Coloring Book

Color your way to Christmas Day!

Count down the 24 days before Christmas with this fun-filled coloring book. Find a full-page picture and other delightful illustrations to color every day. On December 1st, begin by reading part of the Nativity story and coloring the picture on the next page. On each following day, read more of the Nativity story and color another beautiful picture. By Christmas Day, you will have a treasure from this special season to keep for years to come!

Use your favorite colored pencils, crayons, or markers for 24 days of coloring fun!

D1299553

First published in the United States of America in 2017 by
Vermont Christmas Company
P.O. Box 1071
Burlington, VT 05402

Questions or comments?
www.VermontChristmasCo.com I info@VermontChristmasCo.com I Toll Free 1.888.890.0005

10 9 8 7 6 5 4 3 2 1

ISBN: 978-0-9987579-0-2

Designed in U.S.A. I Printed in China

Each *DAY*
is a new BEGINNING,
each PAGE is a new
ADVENTURE!

Play...

Have fun...

START COLORING!

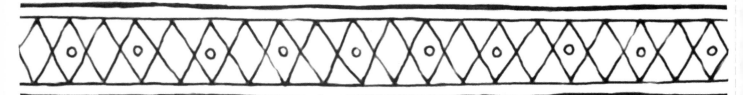

December 1

This is how the BIRTH of JESUS, the LIGHT of the WORLD, happened.

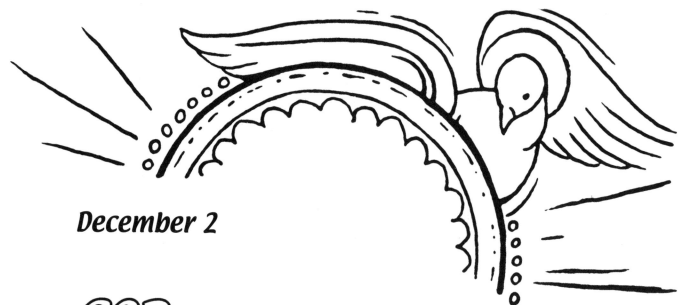

December 2

GOD sent an angel named *GABRIEL* to visit a young woman in *NAZARETH.* Her name was *MARY* and she was engaged to marry *JOSEPH.*

December 3

The ANGEL said to MARY, "Hail, favored one! The LORD is with you."

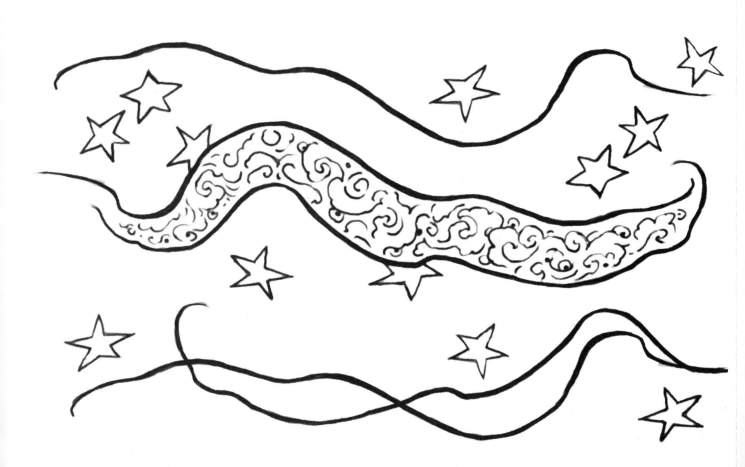

December 4

Then the ANGEL told MARY that she would have a BABY SON and name him JESUS.

December 5

The **ANGEL** also told **MARY** that **JESUS** would be **GOD'S SON,** and that his **KINGDOM** would last **FOREVER.**

December 6

Around the same time, the ROMAN emperor, CAESAR AUGUSTUS, decided that EVERYONE should be COUNTED in a CENSUS.

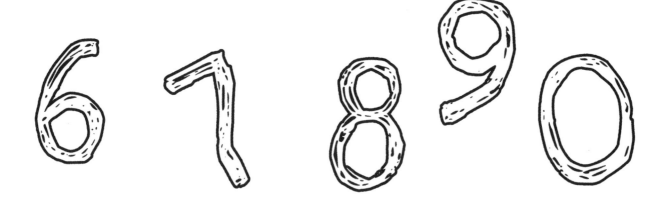

December 7

To be COUNTED, Joseph had to go to BETHLEHEM. Mary went with him, and SHE was ALMOST ready to have her BABY.

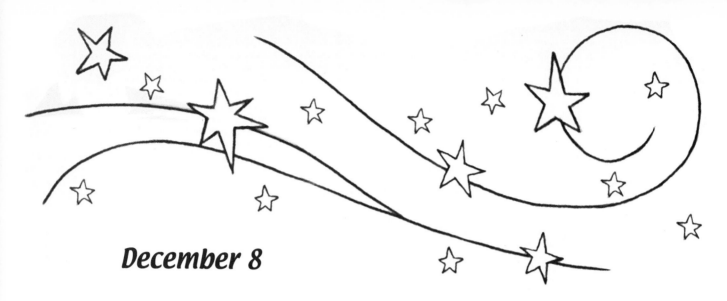

December 8

In BETHLEHEM, Mary gave birth to JESUS. Because there was no ROOM for them in the INN, Mary placed the BABY JESUS on a bed of hay in a STABLE.

December 9

At **NIGHT,** there were **SHEPHERDS** protecting their **FLOCKS** in the fields around **BETHLEHEM.**

December 10

An **ANGEL** appeared to the **SHEPHERDS,** telling them about the **GOOD NEWS** that a **SAVIOR** has been **BORN.**

December 11

The *ANGEL* also told the *SHEPHERDS* that they would find the *SAVIOR* wrapped in *SWADDLING CLOTHES* and lying on a bed of hay in a *STABLE.*

December 12

So the SHEPHERDS went and found MARY and JOSEPH, and the baby JESUS in a stable.

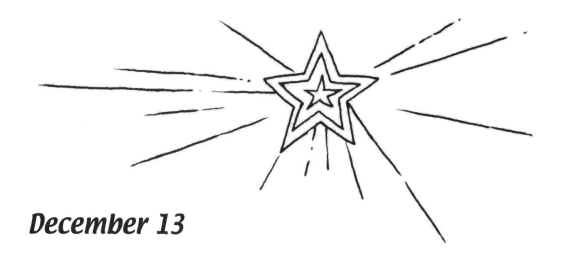

December 13

When the **SHEPHERDS** saw **JESUS,** they explained what the **ANGEL** had said. Everyone who **HEARD** the shepherds was **AMAZED.**

December 14

After JESUS was born, WISE MEN from afar arrived in JERUSALEM. They asked where to find JESUS, who was the NEWBORN KING.

December 15

The *WISE MEN* had been *GUIDED,* to *JESUS* by a *STAR,* and they had come to *HONOR HIM.*

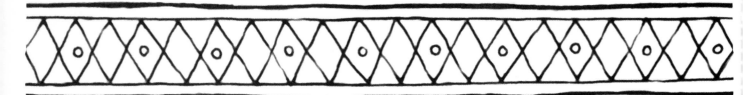

December 16

When **KING HEROD** heard about this, he was **VERY** upset. **PEOPLE** weren't supposed to **HONOR ANYONE** but him.

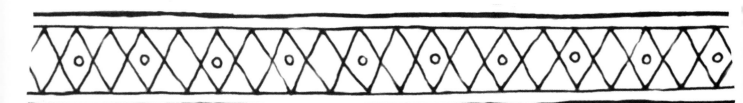

December 17

Herod sent the WISE MEN to LOOK for JESUS. But he also wanted them to RETURN and tell him where Jesus WAS so that he could bring HARM to JESUS.

December 18

When the STAR stopped over Jesus, the WISE MEN were so HAPPY. And when they saw JESUS with Mary, they got down on their KNEES to HONOR HIM.

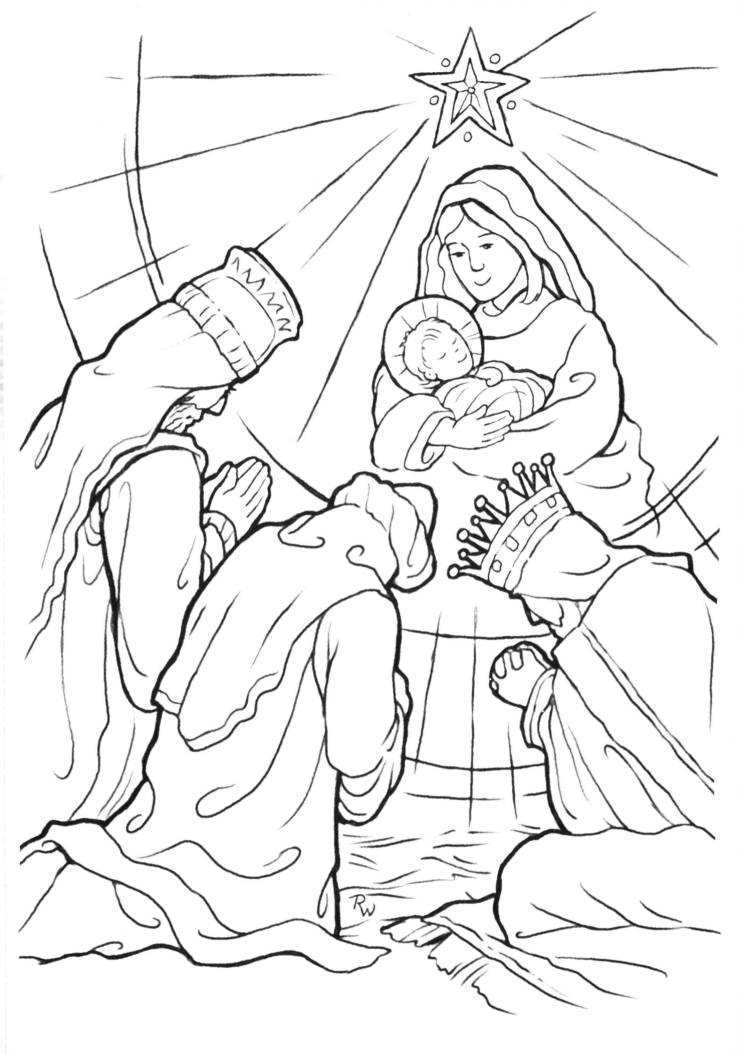

December 19

Then the WISE MEN gave JESUS grand gifts of GOLD, FRANKINCENSE, and MYRRH.

December 20

To protect Jesus, the WISE MEN were WARNED in a DREAM not to return to HEROD. So they LEFT and went HOME another way.

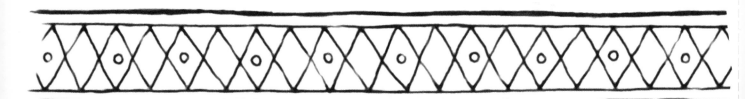

December 21

Next, an *ANGEL* told *JOSEPH* to take *JESUS* and Mary and *FLEE* into *EGYPT,* because Herod's *SOLDIERS* were going to look for and *HARM JESUS.*

December 22

So JOSEPH took JESUS and MARY in the dark of the NIGHT and they quickly left for EGYPT. Later, after Herod died, the FAMILY returned to NAZARETH.

December 23

Over **TIME**, Jesus **GREW** and became **STRONG**. He was a very **WISE CHILD**, and **GOD WATCHED** over him.

December 24

A *CHILD* is *BORN* to us,
a *SON* is given us;
and upon *HIS SHOULDER*
dominion *RESTS.* They
name him
WONDER-COUNSELOR,
GOD-HERO,
FATHER-FOREVER,
PRINCE OF PEACE!

ABOUT the ARTIST

Freelance illustrator Randy Wollenmann has been working in the decorative arts for over 30 years developing artwork for a broad range of markets; from tabletop giftware, dinnerware, and glass designs, to greeting cards, gift wrap, puzzles, books, and children's learning materials. With his first years spent at Abbey Press, owned by the Benedictine Monks of the St. Meinrad Archabbey, Randy set the direction his work would take. Over the years he has developed a diverse collection of artwork with many images coming back time and again to the inspiring design and vivid color of stained glass. "It's a constant source of joy, to think back on my first experiences of looking at the grand and intricate stained glass windows at the monastery church. The light piercing through all that colorful textured glass and the stories that came to life as the light danced around the many scenes continues to inspire me today."